vision

HOW, WHY AND WHAT WE SEE

By JANETTE RAINWATER

Illustrated By WEIMER PURSELL

GOLDEN PRESS   NEW YORK

Library of Congress Catalog Card Number 62-9856

What is Sight?

Have you ever wondered what it would be like to be unable to see? We would not know if the sky were blue or if the mountains were capped with snow. We could not watch a ball game or go to a movie. We could not enjoy the sight of a gull wheeling over a calm sea or a giant ocean liner steaming into port. All the color and variety of form which fills the world around us would be absent.

If you were blindfolded and given a flower, you might be able to identify it as a rose or a lilac by touch or smell. Probably you have gone into a familiar room and stumbled about in the dark while searching for a light switch. With most people, the senses of touch and smell are secondary because of their dependence on an initial sight impression. Because *seeing* is the basic sense on which we depend for our impressions of the world, man can well be termed a visual creature.

Those who study vision find that man's seeing depends on three things. First, there must be light. Second, the person must have a brain, nerves, and eyes that are in working order. Third, *what* he sees and *how* he sees will vary according to his interests, previous experience, and personality.

No animal, not even a cat, can see in complete darkness. We can "see" an object such as an apple only because it is lighted. Light rays strike the apple and are reflected in all directions from its surface. We can see the apple only if some light rays from a powerful enough source enter our eyes.

Light is the name we have given to one portion of the tremendous range of energy that is constantly radiating from the sun. Television waves, radio waves, infra-red rays, x-rays, and cosmic rays are other portions of that energy. These types of radiant energy differ from one another only in the length of their waves. Light wave lengths are infinitesimally small, and we measure them in terms of a unit called an *angstrom*. One inch equals *250 million* angstroms. The human eye can "see" only those wave lengths that are from 4000 angstroms to 8000 angstroms long. These wave lengths we have named *light*.

To show the range of the electromagnetic radiation spectrum, this simplified diagram was plotted on a logarithmic scale. Note the small range of visible light.

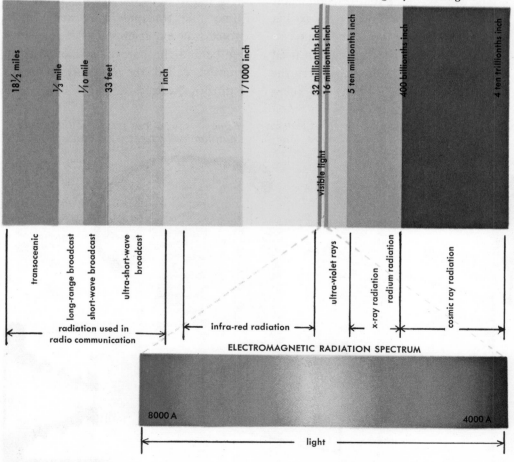

Our Eyes

Many people have compared the human eye to a camera. Light enters both of them through a small opening. The light rays are bent by a lens, and the picture is formed on a material that is chemically sensitive to light—the film of the camera and the retina of the eye.

Superior to the camera, the eye can take unlimited pictures which are catalogued by the mind and stored in the memory for future recall.

The eye is a globe that rests on a soft pad of fatty tissue inside a bony socket of the skull. The eyeball maintains its shape by creating pressure within itself which is as great as the pressure in the surrounding tissues. The eyeball keeps its shape because of the tough outside layer called the *sclera*.

The next layer is the *choroid* which contains many blood vessels. The eye, like the rest of your body, is living tissue and must be supplied with oxygen and food carried by the blood. The innermost layer, the *retina,* contains many delicate nerve cells which receive the picture and send it to the *sight center* of the brain by way of the *optic nerve*.

In the front of the eye the sclera becomes the transparent *cornea* which protects the eye from injury. The chamber behind the cornea is filled with a solution called the *aqueous humour,* Latin for "watery liquid."

The eye is much like a camera. A real inverted image is produced on the retina of the eye as on the film of the camera. The brain automatically rights the image for us.

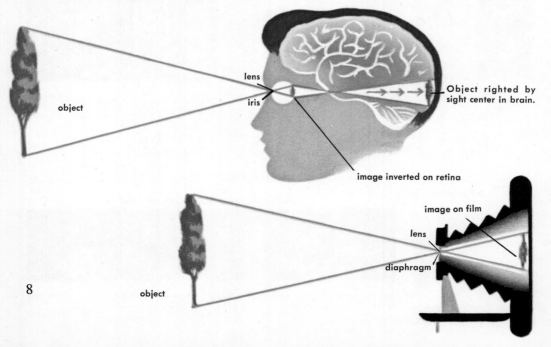

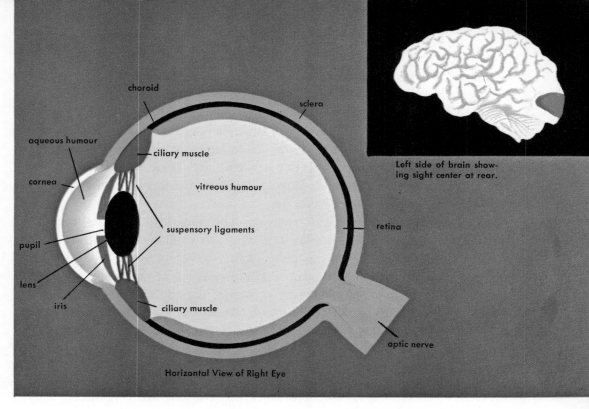

choroid

sclera

aqueous humour

ciliary muscle

cornea

vitreous humour

suspensory ligaments

retina

pupil

lens

iris

ciliary muscle

optic nerve

Left side of brain show-
ing sight center at rear.

Horizontal View of Right Eye

*This cross section of the right eye is shown horizontally. The ciliary
muscles and ligaments support the lens and control its shape.*

When we say a person has blue eyes, or green eyes, or brown eyes, we are describing the color of his *iris*. Most babies of European ancestry are born with blue eyes. A few months later these children's irises change to their permanent color which, (with all other physical characteristics) is determined by heredity. Eye color will depend on that of parents and grandparents.

The iris changes in size very much like the diaphragm of a camera (which is often called an iris). In dim light the iris becomes smaller, making the hole in its center (called the *pupil*) larger, and so letting more light into the eye. In bright light the iris will become larger until sometimes the pupil is not much larger than a pinhole, thus protecting the sensitive retina from too much light.

Depending upon the strength of the light source, the pupil dilates and contracts.

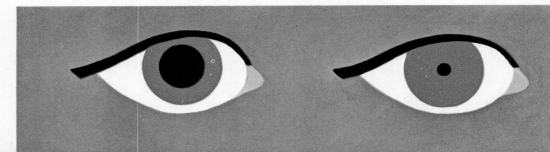

Behind the iris is the *lens* of the eye. It is a soft, transparent structure. The cornea, the aqueous humour and the lens bend or refract the light rays entering the eye so that they come to a sharp focus on the retina. This bending is due to a property of light. Light travels most easily through empty space. When it passes through glass or water or any other transparent matter, it slows down. In water it travels three-fourths as fast as in air; in glass, two-thirds as fast.

This slowing down causes a light ray to bend when it passes into water (or glass) at an angle to the surface. This bending is called *refraction*. Refraction causes underwater objects to appear larger than they really are. When you look down into the water, it will not seem as deep as you know it is. A stick poked into the water will appear to bend upward toward the surface.

Because light rays bend at a glass surface we have lenses that can focus light.

Even more important, our eyes can see apples or any other object before our eyes because the light rays from the various objects are bent by the corneas and lenses of our eyes. Thus the form, shape and color of objects are duplicated on the much smaller area of the retina.

The image formed on the retina is upside down and is reversed from right to left. We are not aware of this inversion and reversal, as our brains are able to decode the information from the retina and keep our world from seeming topsy-turvy. A psychologist once tried wearing special lenses in front of his eyes which registered the things he saw "correctly" on his retina. But everything seemed upside down and backwards to him. He was quite confused, and he had difficulty in doing such simple things as eating and walking. It took him eight days to become accustomed to his new way of seeing the world.

Centuries ago, an Arab mathematician, Alhazen, demonstrated refraction.

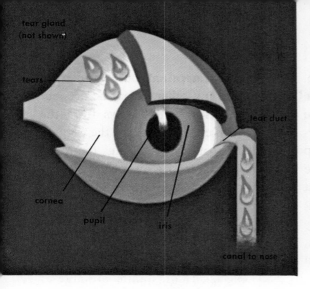

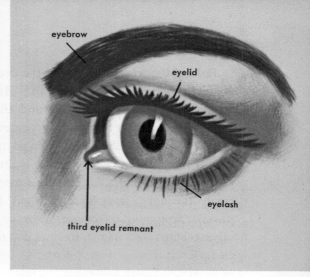

Tear glands produce salty drops that bathe the eyeball and drain into the nose.

The outer organs of the eye serve a primarily protective purpose.

The area between the lens and retina is filled by the *vitreous humour*, a transparent, jelly-like substance. Its pressure maintains the eyeball's shape and keeps the retina in place.

Since the eye is such an important and such a delicate part of the body, it is fortunate that it has so many accessory organs to protect it. The *eyebrow* shields the eye from too vivid light and from perspiration. The upper and lower *eyelids* are movable shades that cover the eye when you are asleep. They act also as automatic windshield wipers to keep the surface of the eyeball moist. Almost everyone blinks about once every 2½ seconds. The eyelids also blink to protect the eye from a sudden bright light or a foreign object. Projecting from the edges of the eyelids are the short hairs that we call *eyelashes*.

A *tear gland* at the outer corner of the eye manufactures tear-water which enters the eye through *tear ducts* to the upper eyelid. These tears are constantly washed over the outer surface of the cornea by the blinking eyelids, killing some germs and keeping our eyes moist.

There are two canals below the eye which carry off the used tears so they will not run down the cheeks. If a foreign object gets into the eye or if a person is under some emotional stress, the tear glands produce an excess amount of fluid which we call "crying."

The pink area in the corner of the eye near the nose is no longer of any use. It is all that remains of a *third eyelid* which is present in some other animals and which winks across the eye from the inside corner to the outside. Polar bears have a semi-transparent third eyelid which they can keep closed to relieve their eyes from the glare of the snow. Rabbits protect their eyes with their third eyelids when they go through thorny bushes. Parrots use their third eyelid to cleanse their eyes.

11

Kinds of Vision

The retina is made of nerve tissue which in the developing unborn baby was part of the brain itself. There are about 137 million sight-receiving cells located in the retina which connect with about one million "telephone lines" that in turn connect with the sight center of the brain.

The sight-receiving cells are of two different kinds; *cones* and *rods*. Things seen by the cones and by the rods are so different that we could almost say that we have two eyes in one.

The cones are used for seeing color and for noticing small detail, and are useful only in a good light.

The rods can see shape and movement in very dim light, but cannot distinguish color or notice small detail such as the words on this page.

Most of the cones are concentrated in a very small area directly behind the lens, called the *fovea*. The fovea contains no rods. Beyond the fovea the cones are scattered among the rod cells. At the edges of the retina there are no cones, only rods.

We read by focusing the light rays from the words onto the fovea a few letters at a time, then moving our eyes so that the next few letters can be focused on the fovea and so on. Children learn to read by learning to recognize different letters and different words, and also by learning to move their eyes efficiently.

Try to fix your attention on one word on this page. You will be able to see, although not too sharply, your hands holding the book and the furniture in the room. If someone beside you moves, you will be able to see him out of the corner of your eye. You see these fringe objects mostly with your rods.

The rods and cones in the retina receive many dots of light which form a complete image as do the many dots which form the halftone engraving below.

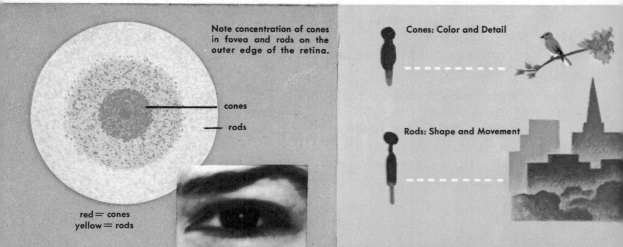

Note concentration of cones in fovea and rods on the outer edge of the retina.

cones

rods

red = cones
yellow = rods

Cones: Color and Detail

Rods: Shape and Movement

A change in lighting causes the Arch of Triumph to look different at night.

If you are outdoors at twilight, reading becomes increasingly difficult until finally it is impossible. You will gradually lose your ability to distinguish colors. A red lawn chair will look black at a time when you can still see that the grass is green.

When the light is quite dim, your fovea will be useless since it is composed entirely of cones. If you want to see something at night, such as a star or a distant ship, do not look directly at it for the light rays will then fall on the fovea. Instead, look a little to one side or the other to make use of your rods.

Our eyes, in adapting to darkness, become ten thousand times more sensitive to light than when they are adapted to brightly-lit surroundings. The human eye sees light too faint for a camera's light meter. Some animals have even better night vision. (See page 34.)

This vision is possible because of a chemical substance in the rods called *visual purple*. Visual purple is bleached out by light. It decomposes in light and regenerates, or reforms, in darkness. You have probably had the experience of entering a dark place, such as a movie theater, in the daytime. At first nothing can be seen except the bright screen. After a few minutes, however, the dimness around you begins to lift and you can distinguish objects and people. The action of visual purple has been renewed.

During World War II pilots either wore goggles containing pure red filters or stayed in a darkened room for an hour before going out on a night flight. This protected their visual purple. Vitamin A is necessary for the rebuilding of visual purple. People who do not eat enough foods containing Vitamin A suffer from night blindness.

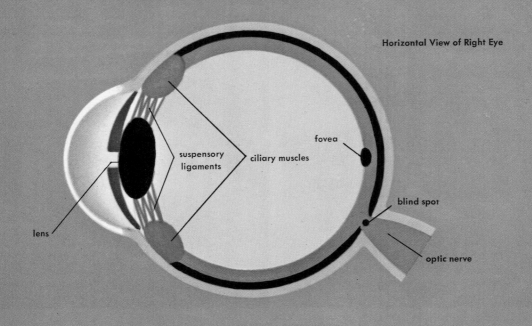

fovea

blind spot

suspensory
ligaments

ciliary muscles

optic nerve

lens

The Blind Spot In Your Eye

Every eye has a *blind spot*. All the million nerves to the brain combine to form one "cable," the *optic nerve,* which leaves the retina through a hole at a point near the fovea. At this point the absence of sight-receiving cells creates a blind spot.

To find your blind spot, close your left eye and hold two pencils with eraser tops in front of your right eye. Keeping your eye focused on one of the erasers, move the other one slowly to the right. If you keep your eye still, the moving eraser will disappear from sight for an interval and then reappear further right.

Or look at the square below with your right eye and you will not be able to see the dot. But if you look at the dot with your right eye, you will be able to see the square. How would you find the blind spot in your left eye by using the square and the dot? (Turn the book upside down.)

We are not usually conscious of our blind spots, because our eyes are usually moving all the time that we are seeing. So no object can be "lost" on the blind spot for very long. Also, each eye can usually see the object that is lost on the other eye's blind spot.

Seeing Near and Far

The light rays entering the eyeball are bent first by the cornea, then a little more by the aqueous humour and by the lens so that they fall into a sharp focus on the retina.

The light rays coming from close objects need to be bent more than the light rays coming from distant objects.

The eye has the marvelous power of *accommodation* in order to do this job. The soft and elastic lens is normally held tight in a stretched-out position by the *suspensory ligaments*. In this "at rest" position the eye can focus on objects from 20 feet away or further.

When the eye needs to focus on something closer, the *ciliary muscles* contract and force the suspensory ligaments to relax. This allows the lens to bulge out into a position in which it can bend the rays enough to focus the image of a nearby object on the retina.

A camera cannot change the shape of its lens. A camera focuses by moving the lens out to the proper position. There are inexpensive cameras which have only one position for the lens. Close-up pictures taken by such a camera are likely to be out of focus and blurred.

Focusing. *The normal eye, by use of the ciliary muscles and suspensory ligaments thickens the lens to see near objects and flattens the lens to see distant ones.*

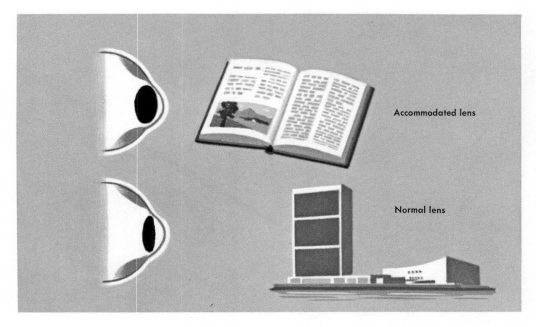

Accommodated lens

Normal lens

The picture formed on the retina has no meaning until it is sent by tiny electric discharges to the brain. It is in the *sight center* of the brain that the most important part of seeing takes place. Here the picture is compared with stored memories of things seen before, and the picture is given meaning. A person, blind from birth, who acquires sight by an eye operation will not be able to recognize anything he sees. He will have to learn the meaning of everything he sees, just as a new-born baby does.

So when we "see" an apple, we know that it is an apple, because it resembles many apples that we have seen before that our brain has catalogued.

How can we see that our apple is a real, three-dimensional apple and not just a good color photograph of an apple? Our eyes receive two different pictures of the apple. The right eye sees further around the right side of the apple than the left one does, and the left eye sees more of the left side. The brain interprets the messages from the two retinas and "sees" the apple as round and having depth.

The stereoscope, an instrument that gives a three-dimensional effect to photographs that are viewed through it, shows two pictures that are slightly different. Each eye sees the scene it would see in real life. The brain "sees" the scene as three dimensional.

Below is seen a somewhat exaggerated example of a typical stereoscopic slide. The two views seen simultaneously give the illusion of three dimensions.

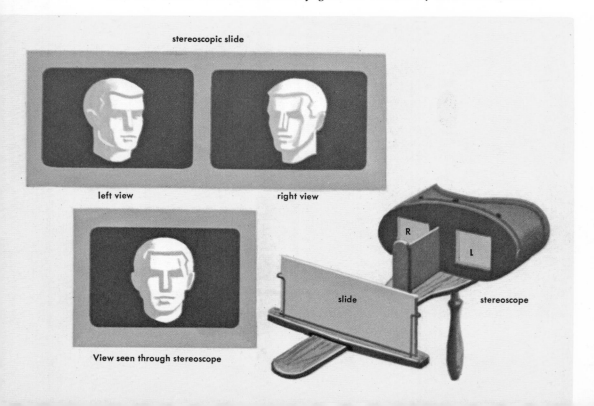

stereoscopic slide

left view

right view

View seen through stereoscope

R

L

slide

stereoscope

The convergence of the telephone lines, the decreasing size of the poles, and the haziness of the more distant buildings help to create perspective.

How do we know how far away something is? A nearby object will form a larger image on the retina than a far-away object of the same size. If they are familiar objects and the brain knows what size they should be, we will be able to judge how far away each is. Since we know how big apples are, we will know whether a certain apple is within arm's reach or not solely by the size image it makes on the retina.

Placing one object in front of another and making one object larger than another are two cues for distance which don't require both eyes. Artists use these cues and several more to give *perspective,* or the feeling of depth, to their paintings.

OPTICAL ILLUSIONS. *Sometimes the shape or size or distance of an object is misperceived because of the influence of immediate surroundings. This is called an optical illusion. Several examples are found on the next four pages. In Figure 1 the people appear distorted in size because they have been placed in an artificially distorted room.*

Figures 2-4 have within them two lines equal in length. Figures 5, 6, and 8 have parallel lines which only seem to be crooked. A perfect circle in Figure 9 appears misshapen. Circle B in Figure 7 appears larger than Figure A when it is not. And the interrupted line in Figure 10 seems to be two broken ones.

HIDDEN FIGURES. *Surroundings that are sufficiently confusing can make it difficult to see the contour of an object. There is a familiar word hidden in Figure 11. (Cover the top half to find it.) In Figure 12, drawings B and C contain drawing A. Natural and artificial camouflage are seen in Figures 13 and 14.*

REVERSIBLE FIGURES *are those which can be seen in two different ways. Figure 15 is a cube which alternately faces in different directions. The face of an old woman or a young woman with her head turned can be seen in Figure 16. Figure 17 shows the silhouette of a goblet or a double profile.*

REDUCED CUES. *The words YOU CAN READ THIS are easily recognized in Figure 18 although only the tops of the words are printed.*

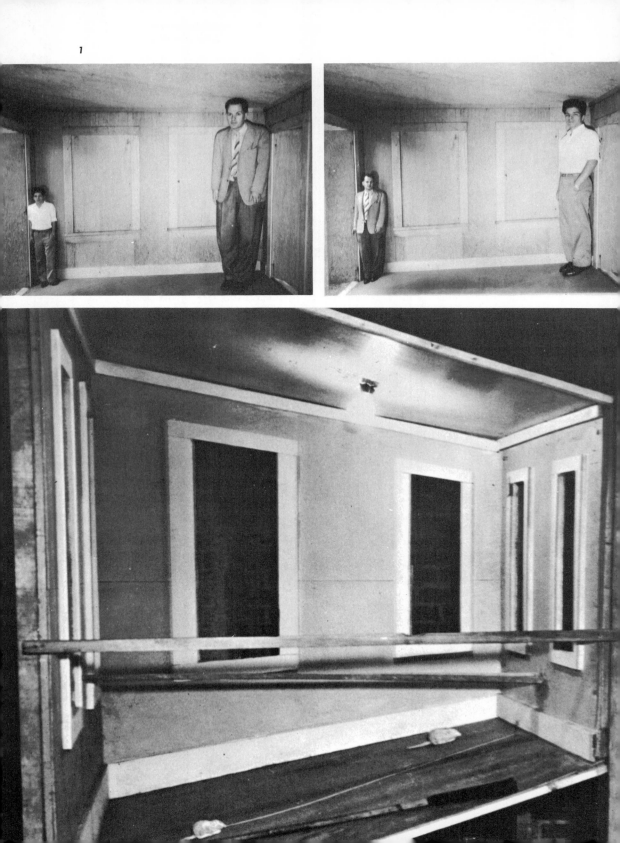

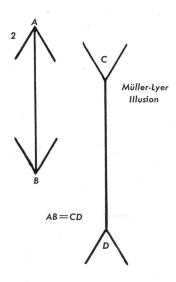

2

*Müller-Lyer
Illusion*

$AB = CD$

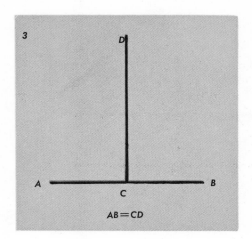

3

$AB = CD$

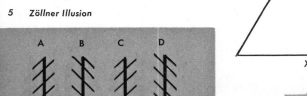

4

$XA = AY$ *Sander Parallelogram*

5 *Zöllner Illusion*

A, B, C, and D are parallel

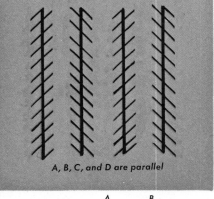

6

*Helmholtz
Illusion*

*A and B are
parallel*

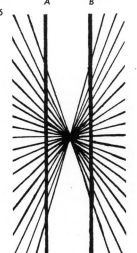

7

A and B are equal

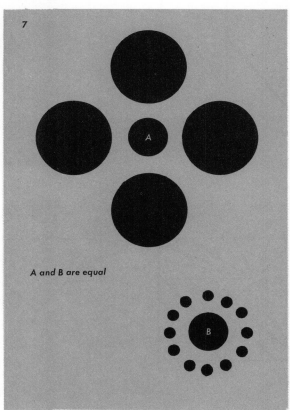

8

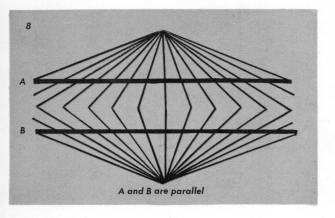

A

B

A and B are parallel

9

The circle is perfect

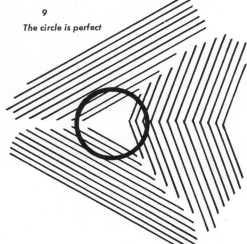

10   Poggendorff Illusion

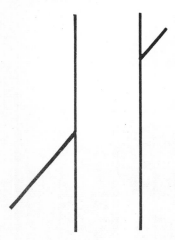

11   What word forms this design?

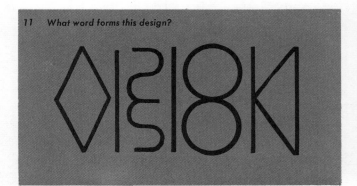

12

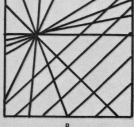

B

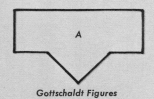

A

Gottschaldt Figures

Find figure A in figures B and C.

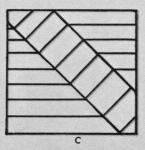

C

13

Natural Camouflage
(Killdeer Eggs)

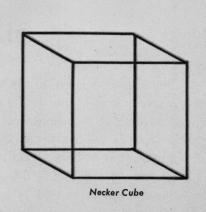

15

Necker Cube

14

Artificial Camouflage

16

Leeper's Figure
(The Wife and the Mother-in-Law)

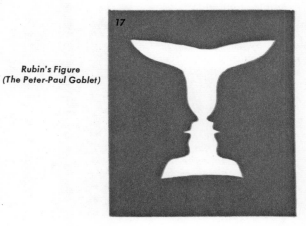

17

Rubin's Figure
(The Peter-Paul Goblet)

18

YOU CAN READ THIS

Objects of Sight

There are so many things to see at any given moment that we cannot really see them all. Which things we select to see depends on our personalities and our interests. Our minds have developed screening devices which filter out the uninteresting sights and bring to our notice only those things we want to see.

A family taking a Sunday afternoon stroll will notice many different things. The father may see the automobiles passing by, the teenage daughter may observe the clothes in the store window, the mother may watch the other people.

The ten-year-old son might see only airplanes, while the two-year-old might become fascinated by a bit of colored glass in a crack in the sidewalk that no one else sees at all.

Some people live all their lives only half-seeing. Such a man might not be able to tell you, for instance, the color of the buses in his home town or what his wife was wearing at breakfast that morning. Artists, scientists and other creative people have the habit of "seeing" as much as they can of everything in their worlds.

People generally see only what interests them. For example, botanists are more alert to leaf structure than most of us. The artist, by use of his imagination, allows us to "see" what is in his mind. Fernand Léger in his "Hommage à Louis David" (right) "sees" a different sort of image than we might if we were looking at the group he has painted. By his arrangement of figures and objects, he has created a picture which shows what he wishes to express. In a sense, we "see" this group of people through Léger's eyes.

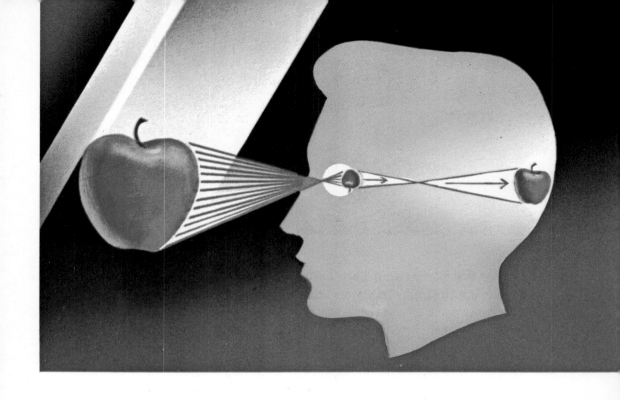

What is Color?

Why does an apple look red? First of all, you are probably looking at the apple in a good light. If you look at it in a very dim light, the apple will look black for the sight-receiving cells in the retina that "see" color are the cones, and cones are useless in dim light.

To see red, you must have good color-sensitive cones. Many animals and some people have cones which are able to see small details distinctly (such as the print on this page), but cannot recognize some or all colors. They are said to be *color-blind*.

The ink used to print the pictures of red objects in this book absorbs light of all other wave lengths except the longest ones. The light reflected from the picture to your eye is of these long wave lengths and produces the sensation of the color red in your brain.

The shortest wave lengths the eye can see give the sensation of violet. Then as the light increases in wave length the color will seem to change from blue to green, yellow, orange, and then to red.

The fundamental experiments demonstrating the nature of color were begun in 1666 by an English scientist, Isaac Newton. *Opticks*, the result of his studies, was published in 1704 and was to cause much controversy.

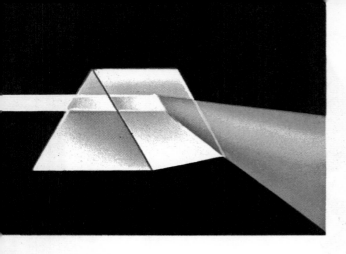

White light entering a prism breaks down into the colors of the spectrum, as seen at the left. It is possible for an inverted prism to recombine the spectrum into white light again.

Newton first placed a prism in front of the sunlight streaming through a hole in a board in his darkened workroom. On a white screen he saw a band of colors which he called a *spectrum*, from the Latin word for *sight*.

The longest waves were bent the least and were red. The shortest waves were bent most by the prism and were violet.

White light, such as sunlight, said Newton, is merely a mixture of light rays of all colors. The prism separates and spreads them. To further prove this he recombined his spectrum into white light with an upside-down prism. Newton was ridiculed for this theory and it was many years before it became generally accepted by scientists.

An object's color is determined by wave lengths coming from a light source.

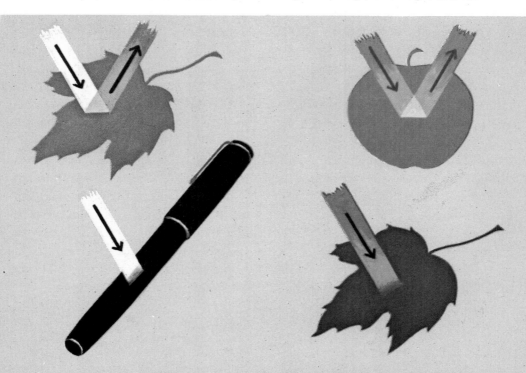

Color then is a sensation dependent principally on the wave lengths of light reflected from the objects in our color-filled world.

Our eyes have a tendency to adapt to the color quality of the existing light. This ability helps us to recognize the "color" of objects when they are seen under different lighting conditions. Noonday sunlight has a nearly even mixture of all wave lengths of light and is called *white light*. An ordinary light bulb gives light that contains more of the long wave lengths than sunlight. If you turn on a lamp in the daytime, the light appears yellow when compared to daylight. You will see that objects lighted by the lamp have slightly different colors than when you see them in daylight. The objects reflect different proportions of the long and short wave lengths under the two kinds of light. But the apparent difference is small because of the adaptation of our eyes and brain.

In extreme cases, however, the colors of light can greatly affect the colors that we see. The light from a neon lamp, for example, contains mostly red rays. Under neon light, green and blue objects look black because they absorb red rays; there are a few green or blue rays to be reflected to produce the sensation of "green" or "blue."

Some fluorescent lamps give a light that is similar to sunlight, yet the wave length distribution is different and contains few red wave lengths. A red automobile seen under a fluorescent street lamp would seem dark brown.

A red apple must be lighted by a source containing long or "red" wave lengths.

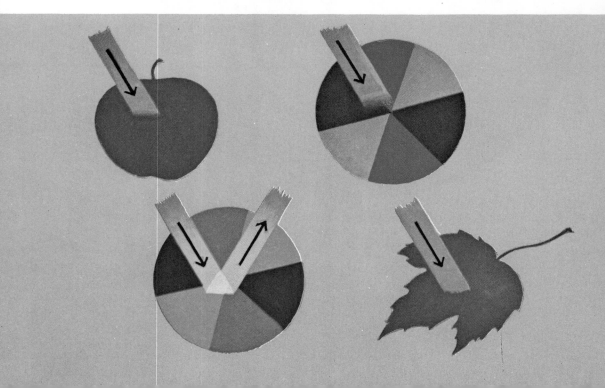

We can distinguish between 100,000 and 300,000 different colors, tints, tones and shades. There are not names for all these different sensations, although the manufacturers of paint and fingernail polish invent many new names for colors every year. Actually any of these many color experiences can be described by one or a combination of seven unique colors: red, green, blue, yellow, white, gray and black. All major color sensations can be arranged on what we call a *color cone*. Think of a double cone, two cones joined at the base.

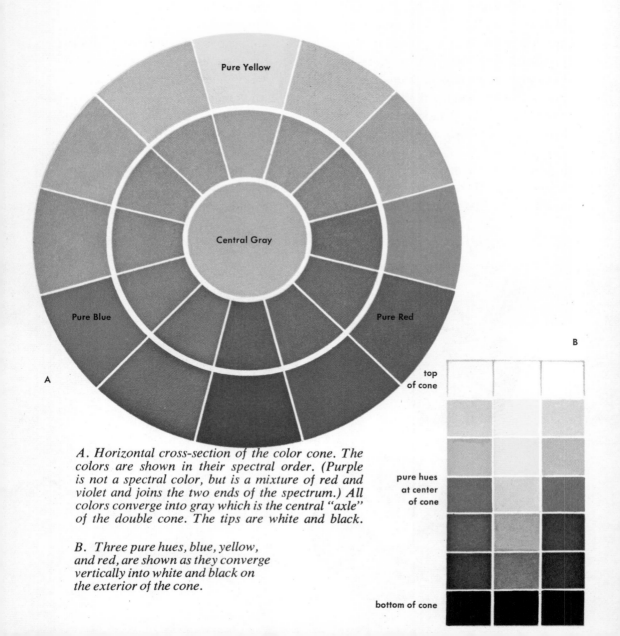

A. Horizontal cross-section of the color cone. The colors are shown in their spectral order. (Purple is not a spectral color, but is a mixture of red and violet and joins the two ends of the spectrum.) All colors converge into gray which is the central "axle" of the double cone. The tips are white and black.

B. Three pure hues, blue, yellow, and red, are shown as they converge vertically into white and black on the exterior of the cone.

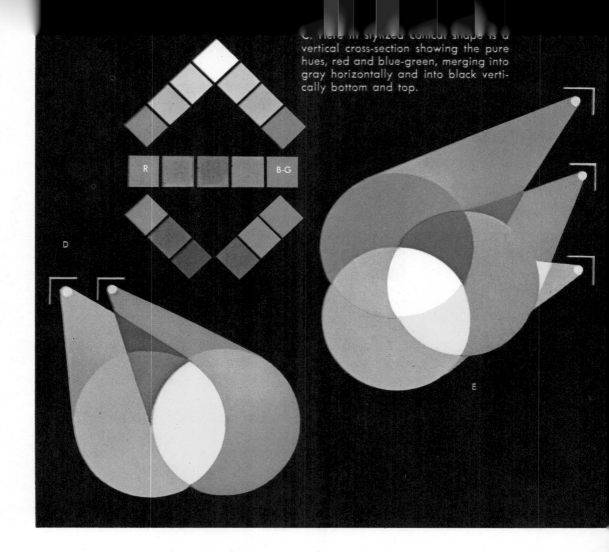

C. Here in stylized conical shape is a vertical cross-section showing the pure hues, red and blue-green, merging into gray horizontally and into black vertically bottom and top.

R

B-G

D

E

The largest circumference of the color cone contains the *circle of pure hues—* red, red-orange, orange, orange-yellow, yellow and so on, in the order of the spectrum, with one color blending into another. (See Figure A, opposite page.)

Each of these pure hues is termed *fully saturated*. They become less saturated and lose their purity as they approach the central column. (Note Figures A, B, and C on these pages.)

White light can be created by projecting beams of red, green and blue light together. Notice that red and green mixed make yellow. (Figure D.)

White light can be created also by using spotlights to combine pairs of complementary colors—those colors lying opposite one another on the hue circle (Figure E). Examples of such pairs are: red and green-blue, green and purple, green-yellow and violet.

27

A negative or complementary after image can be seen after staring at each picture above and then looking at a white piece of paper. What colors do you see?

A bright light bleaches the visual purple of the rods of the retina and rod vision is temporarily lost. (Page 13.) The cones can also become fatigued by seeing too much color, although no chemical similar to visual purple has yet been found there. If you stare at a patch of any color, red for example, for thirty seconds and then look at a piece of white paper, you will then see the complementary color, greenish-blue. The cones have exhausted their ability to respond to red light and can respond only to white light minus red light, greenish-blue light.

You can also see color when there is no color present. If you stare at a brightly colored object and then close your eyes, sometimes you can "see" the object and recognize its color for a very short time afterwards. This is a *positive after-image*. Some people "see" very vivid colors in their dreams and imagi-

nation. Painters can remember exact colors in the same way that musicians can recall exact musical notes.

You can produce color with a black and white disc. Copy the design below on a three-inch square of white cardboard, using a very black ink, preferably India ink, for the black areas. Put a nail through the center and spin the disc in a bright light. You should see red and blue circles. Now spin it in the opposite direction and the positions of the colors should reverse.

The preceding experiments show you that color is a sensation, something we "see" in our brains.

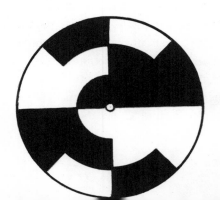

28

Color-Blindness

There are a few people who do not "see" color as most people see it. About one out of every twenty men (and only one-tenth that number of women) have some degree of color-blindness.

Color-blindness is not a disease but a defect of vision that is inherited. A man inherits his color-blindness from his mother, who may or may not be color-blind herself. (If she is not color-blind, she is called a *carrier*.) A color-blind woman will have a color-blind father and a mother who is either color-blind or a carrier. Color-blindness cannot be cured, but most color-blind people have found ways to make up for this lack.

The most usual type of color-blindness is that of the person who cannot distinguish between red or green. His colored world is blue, yellow, black, white and gray. What appears red or green to the normal person he "sees" as varying shades of gray. He is thus disqualified from all professions and occupations which require perfect color discrimination. Doctors, painters, electricians, florists, all need to be able to see color. A color-blind person can

Color-blind people are unable to see the red O and X below.

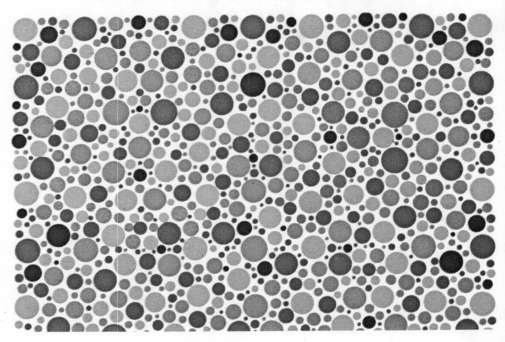

drive safely, as he learns other ways to tell whether the traffic signals are "red" or "green." He can distinguish the relative brightness of the two lights or he notices the position of the lights or observes the behavior of the rest of the traffic. He can look at the traffic light through a red celluloid filter which will transmit only red light.

There are a few color-blind people who can see red and green but who confuse blue and yellow. Then there are a very few who see no color at all, only black, white and gray.

Many different tests have been devised to detect color-blindness. These test plates designed by the American Optical Company contain dots of different sizes, hues, and brightness. The normal person groups the dots on page 29 and sees a circle and X in shades of red; the dots on page 30 form a circle and triangle in green. The totally color-blind person will be unable to see any figure. It is easy for most people to trace a path between the figures, but the color-blind find it difficult to see any clear objects.

We all become less sensitive to blues as we grow older. A chemical change in the lens of the eye will lower the transmission of blue lightwaves. A child, then, can distinguish different shades of blue better than an adult.

Below, a person with normal vision will see a circle and a triangle.

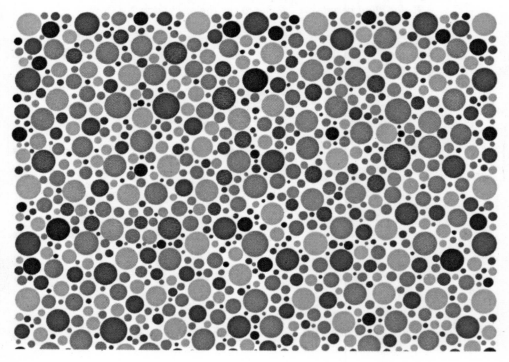

How Cones "See" Color

Color perception, how we "see" color, has puzzled science for many years. Our ability to see color almost certainly depends on the presence of cones in the retina. We are unable to see color at the outer edge of the retina where the rods are located, and we are unable to see color at dusk when the cones cannot respond to a strong light. There are several different scientific theories which try to explain color vision. Each of them explains some of the facts, but none is a completely satisfactory explanation.

According to the *Young-Helmholtz theory,* there are three different kinds of cones: those sensitive to blue light, those sensitive to green light, and those sensitive to red light. The stimulation of these three kinds of cones in varying degrees, it is argued, can produce all the 100,000 or more different sensations of color in the brain. Stimulating the red and green-sensitive cones equally would produce the sensation of yellow. This theory does not explain how a person who is color-blind for red and green can see yellow.

The *Hering theory* proposes that there are three kinds of double-acting cones. One kind is sensitive to blue and yellow light, the second kind is sensitive to green and red light, and the third responds to black and white stimulation. Seeing blue, green and black builds up the substance of the cells. Seeing yellow, red and white breaks down the substance of the cells. Many people do not like this theory because it pairs red and green which are not complementary colors as are blue and yellow.

A third theory, that of Christine Ladd-Franklin, was based on work done on color zones. At the outer edge of the retina no color can be seen, only blacks, whites and grays. Scientists, testing to see which colors can be seen first in indirect vision, found that blue has the largest color zone in the retina, with yellow next. There is a large area of the retina which is not sensitive to red and green but which can "see" blue and yellow. The red-sensitive and green-sensitive zones of the retina are much smaller. The *Ladd-Franklin theory* argues that color vision is a result of evolution. The primitive eye was composed only of rods, and vision was limited to white, black and gray. Then in the central part of the retina the rods evolved into two types of cones. One responded to the long lightwaves with the sensation of yellow, and the other responded to the short lightwaves with the sensation of blue. The yellow-sensitive cones most centrally located further evolved into red-sensitive and green-sensitive cones. Much more research is needed before any of these theories can be accepted or discarded. All have proved useful in stimulating research.

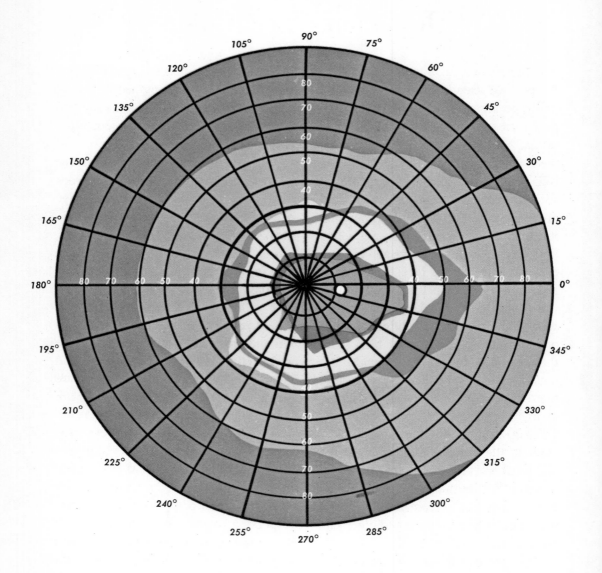

Colors Visible In Indirect Vision

This formalized diagram of the right eye shows the areas in which certain colors are visible when a moderate source of natural light is allowed. The small white circle indicates the blind spot in which no colors are visible. The outer border of each color indicates the furthest range that color is visible in the eye.

How Other Animals See

There are all degrees and kinds of "seeing" in the animal world.

The simplest animals, the amoebae, consist of only one cell each and so of course have no eyes. But they are able to react to light. Some kinds of amoebae move toward the light; some move away from the light.

Slightly more complicated animals have several specialized cells that are sensitive to light. These "eyespots" sense the direction from which light is coming and detect movement in a very primitive sort of way. Insect vision is of a higher order and of a special kind.

Well-developed eyes are found in animals with backbones. These eyes differ according to how the animals live.

Fish do not have eyelids since they live in water. Land animals need eyelids to blink with to keep their corneas moist and clean. Since it is not possible to see very far underwater, fish are normally nearsighted. Those fish that have focusing mechanisms adjust for distant vision, not for near vision as we do.

Many birds have keener vision than we have. The hunting birds—vultures, hawks, and shrikes—can spot very small animals on the ground hundreds of feet below them. If our vision were as keen as theirs, we could read very small print. All the words and pictures in this book could be put on four or five pages. Birds cannot read, not because their eyes are not good enough, but because their brains are not sufficiently developed. Some hunting birds have a fovea of closely packed cones that extends in a band from one side of the retina to the other. With such a fovea we could read long sentences that stretched across several blackboards without having to move our eyes.

frontal-eyed cat   lateral-eyed mouse

Both the fish and the bird have a greater *field of vision* than man. Because our eyes are in the front of our heads and positioned in sockets in our skulls, we cannot see things behind us, above us, and beside us as birds and fish can. They need this wide field of vision to help them escape from their enemies. As a general rule the hunters of the animal world have eyes at the front of their heads; the hunted have eyes at the sides of their heads.

What sort of eyes do mammals have? Again they differ according to where and how the animal lives. The mole, who spends most of his life underground, has crude eyes which can only distinguish light from darkness. Dogs have a very highly developed sense of smell. Their eyes are good at detecting moving objects, but they do not have the fovea of cones needed for seeing ˙ll objects distinctly. An old dog can ⁀d and show very little change in ⁀r, as he gets most of his in-

formation about the world through his sense of smell.

Cats see much better than dogs, and cats see better than we do in dim light. (So do night-active birds, such as the owls.) The cat is able to see distinctly in the daytime by narrowing its pupil to a slit and thus getting a sharp image on the retina. In dim light the cat can enlarge its pupil much more than we are able to in order to let in all the available light.

Of all the mammals only the apes, monkeys, and men have cone vision good enough for reading. Apes and monkeys also have color vision similar to that of man. Rabbits, squirrels, horses and possibly domestic cats are other mammals who may see some color. Of the other animals, some species of birds, snakes, turtles, amphibians, fish, and insects have some form of color vision. It is suspected that bees and some birds can see hues beyond blue that we cannot see.

Improving Imperfect Vision

As we have seen, the eye is a very precisely designed instrument. When you think how much people vary in height and in width and in shape, it is amazing that we all have eyeballs that are so very much the same size and shape.

There are some individual variations, however, and these variations can make a great deal of difference in the kind of vision we have.

Suppose you have an eyeball that is longer than the perfect length for an eyeball. The light rays will bend too soon and come into focus in front of the retina. This condition is called *myopia,* or nearsightedness. Spectacles containing concave lenses, which cause the light rays to spread apart before reaching the lens of the eye, will enable the nearsighted person to see as distinctly as persons with normal vision.

Farsighted people may have eyeballs that are too short. The light rays do not bend soon enough to come into focus on the retina. Spectacles containing convex lenses, which cause the light rays to bend more quickly, will enable the farsighted person to see distinctly. Deviations from the perfect shape of the eye lens will cause nearsightedness and farsightedness as well as more complicated disorders.

Nearsighted people can see objects close at hand distinctly. But distant objects become less clear the further away they are. Books are easily read, but even the large words on the blackboard are blurred and either difficult or impossible to read. A friend across the street is recognized by the color of his clothes or his manner of walking, but not by his facial features. For a nearsighted person such vision is "normal" and he does not realize that he has not been seeing as other people do until he sees the world through concave lenses for the first time.

Myopic people use a concave lens to focus light rays properly on the retina.

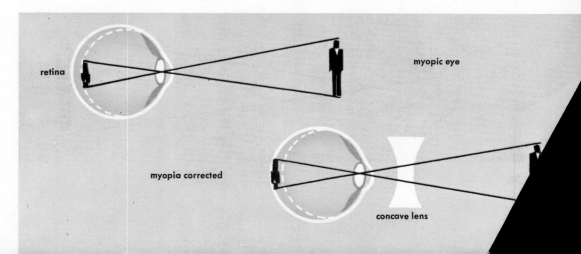

retina

myopic eye

myopia corrected

concave lens

A person with a small degree of far-sightedness may be able to see without eyeglasses by using his ciliary muscles. The lens of his eye will thus become more strongly curved and will bend the light rays enough so that they will come into focus on his retina. This constant use of his muscles for accommodation will be tiring, and the person may suffer from headaches and eyestrain. Many farsighted people do not realize that their vision is impaired until an eye examination reveals the fact.

Why do people have these extra-long or extra-short eyeballs that cause them to be nearsighted or farsighted? No one knows exactly, but part of the reason is probably hereditary. Farsighted parents are apt to have farsighted children and nearsighted parents frequently have nearsighted children.

The normal baby is born with a far-sighted eye, one that is two-thirds the ideal length from front to back. The eyeball gradually lengthens until it reaches the proper length at the age of nine or ten. Most young children are a little farsighted.

Some people think that nearsighted-ness is an over-growth on the part of the eye. Others think that nearsightedness is an effort of the organism to adapt to the increasing amount of close work that our modern civilization demands of us. With the development of lenses, our choice of occupation is no longer seriously limited by peculiarities of our eyesight.

Farsighted people use a convex lens to focus light rays properly on the retina.

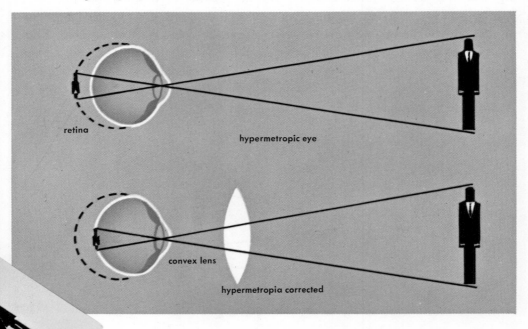

retina

hypermetropic eye

convex lens

hypermetropia corrected

Aging and Sight

Part of the normal process of body aging is the loss of elasticity of the lens. Thus the *near point,* the closest point from his eyes at which a person can see small objects distinctly, will recede as he grows older.

At the age of ten, a person with a normal eyeball and lens can hold small print two inches from his eyes and be able to read it. At 30, he will have to hold it six inches away in order to read it. At 45, he will have to hold it at least a foot away. It is too fatiguing to work at the near point continuously, so most people who do any amount of close work—reading, sewing, etc.—usually have visited an eye doctor and wear glasses for reading and other close work by the time they have reached 45. For farsighted people this loss of the accom-modative power of the lens, or *presby-opia,* becomes evident at a younger age. Nearsighted people can wait longer for their reading glasses. If they are sufficiently nearsighted, they will never need glasses to read at all. However, they will always require concave lenses to see clearly things ten feet away.

Many people over forty need two sets of eyeglasses—one for distant vision and one for near vision. Benjamin Franklin, annoyed by the bother of having to change glasses, designed the first pair of bifocals in 1760. These are eyeglasses which contain a prescription for distant vision in the top portion and a prescription for near vision in the lower portion. Today opticians can grind trifocals, eyeglasses which serve for distant, intermediate and near vision.

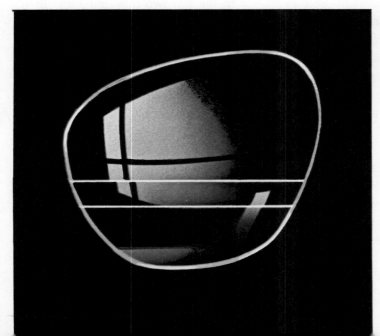

Trifocal lens. *This multi-purpose lens saves many people a great deal of bother by eliminating the constant changing of glasses for different activities.*

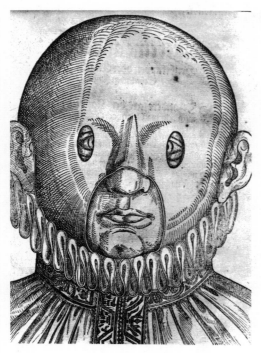

This mask of the 1500's was prescribed to correct strabismus or crossed eyes.

Some people wear *contact lenses*. These plastic or glass shells are moulded to fit the individual eyeball and are worn over the cornea or over the cornea and the sclera. They are much less conspicuous than conventional frame eyeglasses and are often worn by actors and actresses. Some people find them very uncomfortable to wear and cannot wear them for more than a few hours at a time.

Another common defect of vision is *astigmatism*. If either the cornea or the lens is imperfectly curved, the rays of light will be focused as slight blurs and not as perfect points. Such errors can be corrected by grinding an opposite curvature into the lenses of the eyeglasses.

Do the lines of a musical staff seem as clear and sharp horizontally as when turned vertically? At certain angles for an astigmatic person the lines will blur and fuse into a single blob. Farsighted people, nearsighted people, and people with eyeballs of ideal length can all have astigmatism. Small amounts of astigmatism usually go unnoticed, but a pronounced degree of astigmatism will cause headaches and eyestrain and should be corrected by eyeglasses.

Although eyeglasses were invented and used by a few people as long ago as the Middle Ages, it is only in the last hundred years that eyeglasses have become common. It is estimated that eyeglasses are worn or needed by one out of every five school children, two out of every five college students, and two out of every three adults.

Have the eyes of mankind deteriorated in the last two hundred years then? No, our eyes are no worse than those of our ancestors. But until the beginning of universal education it was not necessary for young children to be able to see well for close work. And when the lifespan of the average man was only 35 years, *presbyopia,* a defect normally associated with advanced age, was seldom a problem.

We have records that the same eye problems existed long ago. The educated old men of ancient Greece kept young slaves to read to them. Nearsight-

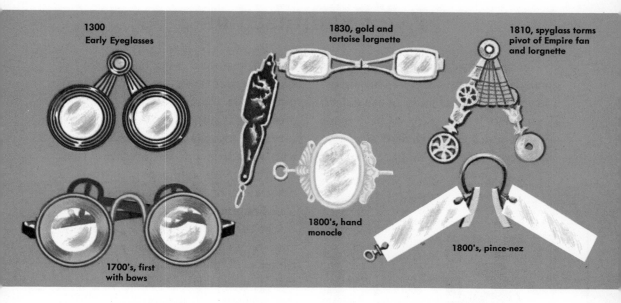

1300
Early Eyeglasses

1830, gold and
tortoise lorgnette

1810, spyglass torms
pivot of Empire fan
and lorgnette

1700's, first
with bows

1800's, hand
monocle

1800's, pince-nez

*Eyeglasses have varied greatly throughout the centuries in both function
and design. Above are a very few representing different periods and uses.*

ed Nero watched his gladiators perform through a concave emerald. During the Middle Ages, many extreme methods were devised by physicians to correct eye defects. Masks which covered the entire head were used to correct such problems as strabismus by forcing the eyes to use the properly placed slits. Glasses of the seventeenth to the nineteenth centuries were often highly decorative, but served chiefly to magnify. We are fortunate to be living at a time when doctors understand the optical system of the eye and can prescribe eyeglasses which will compensate for most defects.

Gentlemen of the Middle Ages had no easy time in seeing through these glasses perched so precariously on their noses.

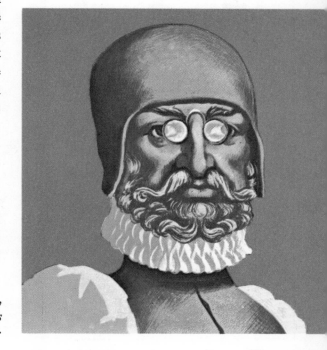

Eye Examinations

The great strides in modern optical science have made it possible for almost every person to overcome an eye defect. If you find it necessary to have your eyes examined, you can visit either an *optometrist* or an *ophthalmologist*. Both are professionals who must pass full state board examinations in order to practice. If there is some eye disease present or if surgery of the eye is necessary, the ophthalmologist is the one who would handle the problem. Both are trained to examine and treat all other kinds of eye defects, such as poor coordination and refractive errors.

The first step in your examination may be to test your distance vision. Either man may well use the chart originated by Snellen in 1862.

A person with normal vision should be able to read the top row at a distance of 200 feet, the second row at a distance of 100 feet, and the following rows at distances of 70, 50, 40, 30, 20, 15, and 10 feet. You will probably be asked to read the chart from a distance of 20 feet. If you can read the letters on the 20 foot line at 20 feet, you have what is called "20/20 vision" or normal vision. If you can read the 10 foot line, your vision is 20/10, or better than average. If the 30 foot line is the smallest one that you can read, your vision is 20/30, or a little less than normal vision. Each eye is tested separately, since it is important to establish the state of health of each eye.

The Snellen Eye Chart at the left was designed to aid all who train in testing distance vision against an accepted norm.

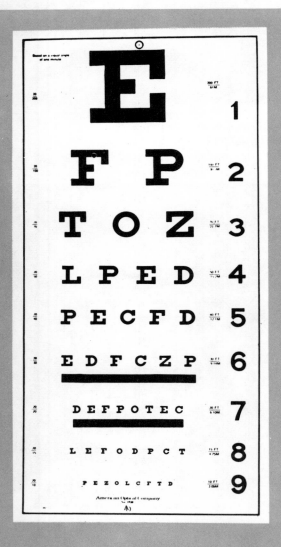

The retinoscope is used to measure the refracting power of the eye.

The doctor can observe the shape and the length of your eyeball by using a *retinoscope*. The mirror reflects light into the eyeball. The doctor, looking through the peephole in the center of the mirror, can see a band of light on your retina and shadows on either side of the band. He will then change the angle of the retinoscope. If your eye is farsighted, the shadow will move in the same direction as the retinoscope. If your eye is nearsighted, the shadow will move in the opposite direction. The doctor has a box of trial lenses of various strengths. He will try first one and then another of these lenses in front of your eye until he finds the exact strength lens needed to make the shadow reverse direction.

He will also ask you to read a chart while looking through eyeglass frames into which he can slip different lenses. He will ask you which lens makes the print most clear and which feels most comfortable. In this way you help to prescribe your own eyeglasses, as these results are compared with the retinoscopy findings before the doctor writes out the final prescription for you to take to the *optician,* the man who grinds the lenses and fits the frames.

Two centuries ago, the testing of vision was far more complicated and far less accurate than today.

The ophthalmoscope is used to investigate the interior of the eye to discover symptoms of disease and to diagnose such ailments as retinal detachment.

This first part of the eye examination can, as we have noted, be performed by an optometrist. He is well acquainted with the functioning of the eye and is able to fit it with glasses to compensate for defects of refraction. He can recognize diseases of the eye, but cannot treat them since he is not a physician. His specialty is physiological optics.

An ophthalmologist, in examining your eyes, may also wish to put drops in your eyes. These drops cause the ciliary muscles to relax for a short time and permit the doctor to observe the eyes when they are unable to accommodate for near vision. They also cause the pupils to dilate, enabling the physician to see more of the eye's interior.

He will examine the interior of the eye with an *ophthalmoscope,* an instrument invented by Helmholtz in 1851.

The interior of the eye is the only place in which the nerves and blood vessels can be seen in their active, living state. With the ophthalmoscope the doctor can detect symptoms of many different diseases of the whole body, such as diabetes, kidney disease, tuberculosis, high blood pressure, and arteriosclerosis. In addition, the ophthalmoscope is used to diagnose eye diseases such as glaucoma and retinal detachment. If a flying sliver of steel should become imbedded in a workman's eye, the eye physician would locate the exact position of the sliver with the ophthalmoscope and then pull the sliver out with an electromagnet.

There are a number of eye diseases which, if left untreated, will result in blindness. Fortunately, ophthalmology has made great advances in the last thirty years.

Glaucoma, or hardening of the eyeball, is a disease in which the pressure of the aqueous humour increases until it eventually destroys the optic nerve. In early stages of the disease the ophthalmologist can lower the pressure by special eye drops or by an operation which creates a new outlet for the aqueous humour.

Today in all civilized countries a drop of silver nitrate solution is put into the eyes of babies just a few minutes after they are born. This prevents the occurrence of a kind of blindness which babies can contract from mothers who have the disease called *gonorrhea.* Little more than one hundred years ago one-fourth of all blindness was caused by gonorrhea. This figure is far smaller today.

Some people are blind or near-blind because their corneas are not transparent and the light cannot get through. Some of these people were born with defective corneas and others had their corneas infected by disease or damaged by an accident. Many of these people can now be made to see again by an operation in which a small window is cut into the damaged cornea and replaced by a transplant from a clear, healthy cornea. There are so called eye "banks" in most countries. People may give their eyes to these eye banks for use after their deaths to enable other people to see.

The formation of cataracts is a common cause of loss of sight in older people. A *cataract* is any clouding of the lens of the eye. Some cataracts remain stationary. Others progress with age, preventing more and more of the light from entering the eye. When the cataract reaches a certain stage, the eye surgeon will usually recommend an operation in which he removes the entire lens. Light can then reach the retina unobstructed, but without a lens it cannot be be focused there. Eyeglasses must then be worn to do the job of refraction that the lens of the eye did before.

Eyeglass Prescriptions

If your eye doctor decides that wearing glasses will help you to see better, he will give you a prescription to take to your *optician*. It might look something like the picture below.

After you get your glasses, the eye doctor will probably ask you to bring them to his office so that he can check to be sure they were ground correctly.

You can make a very rough inspection check yourself. Hold your glasses about a foot away and inspect some object through each lens separately. Move the lens back and forth. If the object moves with the lens, you have a correction for nearsightedness. If the object moves against the lens, the correction is for farsightedness. Keep your eye on some straight-edged object while rotating the lens. If the object keeps its straight edge without any breaks, there is no correction for astigmatism present. The lens for farsightedness magnifies more and has the positive prescription.

You can often tell whether your friends are farsighted or nearsighted just by looking at them closely when they are wearing their glasses. If their eyes appear smaller than usual, they are wearing a correction for nearsightedness; if larger than usual, they are wearing a correction for farsightedness.

The prescription indicates a correction for myopia and a degree of astigmatism.

No. 6826   JANUARY 1962

Mr. H. Z. HUDSON, 8265 SHADYSIDE, MIDDLETOWN

Age 30

History none previous

	Sph.	Cyl.	Axis	Prism	Base	V. A.	Add.	Seg. Dec.
R	−2.00	−0.50	180					
L	−2.25	−0.75	180					

Description dark hornrim	Eyesize	Eyeshape	Fee 20.00
PD	Arm	Bridge Size	Height	Incl.	Deposit 5.00
Pads or Gds.		Spg.	Stud	Due 1/62
Style Temple		Tot. Lgth.	Fv. Lgth.	Call 1/5/62
Form B		PRINTED IN U.S.A.		985A

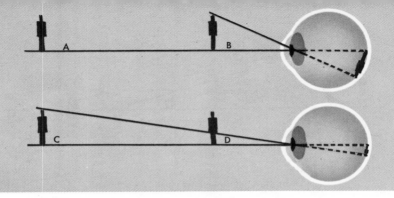

Close Vision

Everyone has noticed that close objects seem larger than far away objects of the same size. This is because a larger image is formed on the retina. In the picture above, figures A, B, C, and D are the same height. The figure B, being closer to the eye, forms a larger image on the retina than the figure C.

Suppose you want to examine the fine detail of some object such as the tip of your finger. You focus both eyes on the fingertip and move it closer to your eyes. At a point perhaps ten inches from your eyes, your fingertip will begin to get blurred if you move it any closer. The point just before blurring occurs is called the *distance of most distinct vision*. Your eyes cannot accommodate any more, and you will not be able to see any more detail of your fingertip without an optical instrument.

But if you place a magnifier—a simple convex lens—close to one of your eyes, you can move your finger very much closer until your fingertip suddenly appears in sharp focus. It will seem very big, and you will be able to examine the ridges and valleys of your finger skin.

You will be seeing a virtual image of your fingertip which is formed at the distance of most distinct vision, or about ten inches from your eye.

A virtual image is an image that cannot be caught on a screen. A real image *can* be caught on a screen. Your reflection in a mirror is a *virtual image;* the picture captured on film is a *real image*.

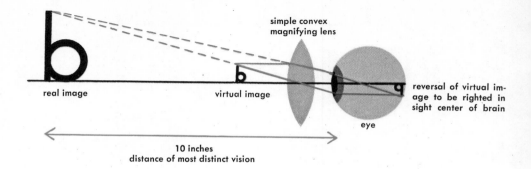

simple convex
magnifying lens

real image

virtual image

reversal of virtual image to be righted in sight center of brain

eye

10 inches
distance of most distinct vision

If the magnifier you are using is labeled 3x, it is a 3-power magnifier. Your fingertip will appear three times as wide and long as it did when you held it at the distance of most distinct vision.

Magnifiers, or *simple microscopes* as they are sometimes called, are used by many older people to read fine print, by watch repairmen to examine the intricate interiors of watches, and in industry to read dials and gauges accurately.

Simple microscopes seldom magnify more than ten times. To make very small things appear large a *compound microscope* is used. This is the kind of microscope that the doctor's laboratory technician uses to make routine examinations of blood. It magnifies between 50 and 1000 times.

It is made of two convex lenses. The first one, the *objective,* forms an enlarged real image of the object. The second lens, or *eyepiece,* further magnifies the image and forms a virtual image

The compound microscope is commonly used in laboratory work to detect disease, study cell structure and various organisms.

46

which the eye sees. The object will seem upside-down to the brain, as the brain is used to reversing the images sent to it by the retina. The compound microscope below is topped by a camera used to photograph slides under observation.

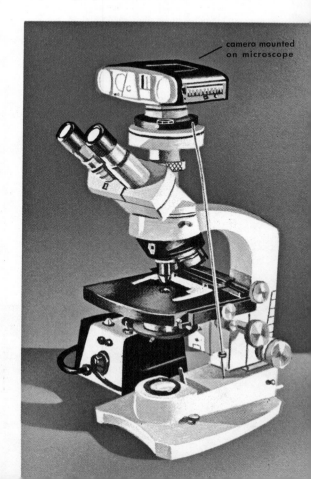

camera mounted on microscope

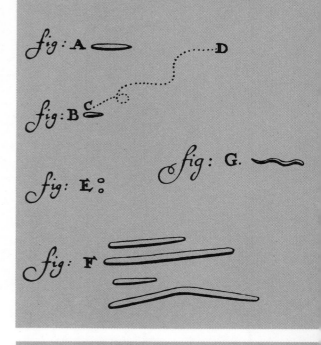

Although lenses were known as long ago as the Roman Empire, no one used a microscope to look at the things around him and to record what he saw —until the seventeenth century. In Holland, Anton van Leeuwenhoek spent his leisure time making lenses and looking through them at new and exciting things. He was the first person to see red corpuscles in human blood and the first to see the striations of muscle fiber.

One day he scraped the white film off his teeth and examined it under his microscope. He saw "little animals, more numerous than all the people in the Netherlands, and moving about in the most delightful manner." Thus he was the first man to observe bacteria. And he used a simple microscope.

At the same time in England another microscopist, Robert Hooke, looked at a piece of cork and found that it was made of "cells much like a honeycomb." The point of a needle was "a multitude of holes and scratches." The edge of a razor was "like a plowed field of ridges and furrows."

With the improved compound microscope of the nineteenth century scientists could identify the different disease-carrying bacteria under the microscope.

The first recorded pictorial representation of bacteria (from the human mouth) was made by Anton von Leeuwenhoek in 1683.

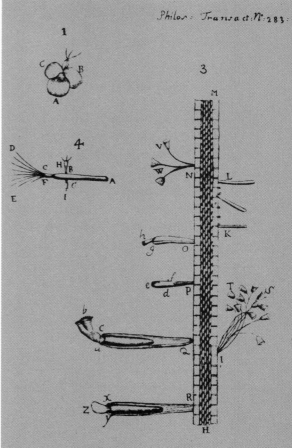

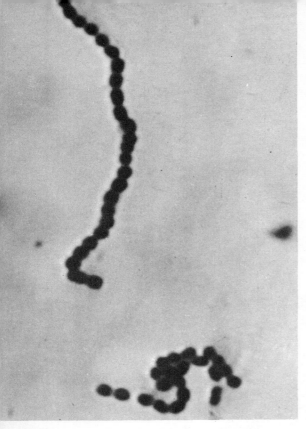

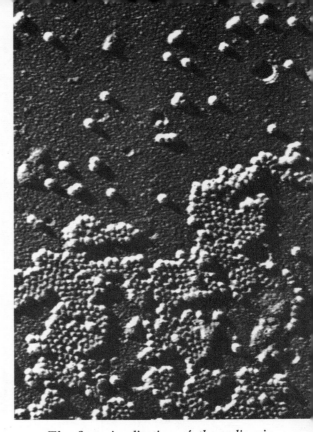

A streptococcus photomicrograph taken with an electron microscope.

The first visualization of the polio virus, an electronmicrograph. (60,000X)

We have learned much of what we know about how our bodies are made and how they work, and much of what we know about diseases since the invention of the microscope.

The microscope is an important tool for the laboratory technician. With it he examines samples of urine for signs of disease. He counts the number of red and white corpuscles in a sample of blood. Microscopes are used in hospitals to examine pieces of tissue from inside the body.

A photomicrograph of pneumococci, a common pneumonia-causing bacteria.

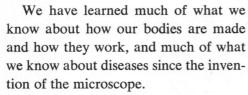

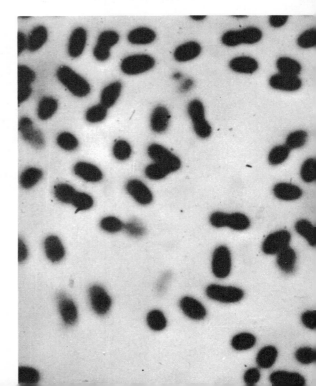

48

The microscope extends our vision in many other fields, too. Geologists use it to study rocks. Engineers can examine steel and other metals for weaknesses. Cotton manufacturers check the weave of their cloth through a microscope. And the FBI looks at finger prints by means of a microscope.

Compound microscopes can magnify as much as 1500 times the width of an object. The smallest object you can see with a compound microscope is about ½ the wave length of light, or about $\frac{1}{100,000}$ of an inch. To see things smaller than this, an entirely new kind of instrument, the *electron microscope,* is used.

An electron is about 100 million times smaller than the wave length of light. Because it is so much smaller, it can be used to investigate things much smaller than the wave length of light, even as small as molecules themselves. A beam of fast electrons is used to cast a shadow of the object on a photographic plate or on a fluorescent screen. With the electron microscope scientists have seen viruses many times smaller than bacteria, and they have located positions of atoms in crystals and molecules.

The electron microscope (right) is one of the most important inventions of modern physics. It can magnify an object over 100,000 times. It can resolve fine detail 20 times better than the best optical microscope, and about 10,000 times as well as the naked eye. With the electron microscope, man is at last almost able to see the individual atoms which John Dalton predicted possible in 1805.

Distance Vision

We use a *telescope* to see things which are far away. Like the compound microscope, the *refracting telescope* uses a convex lens for an objective and another convex lens for the eyepiece. The objective of the telescope is less powerful (less curved) and is much larger in diameter than that of the microscope. We see distant stars and galaxies by their own light. We cannot illuminate them as we can the objects on the stage of the microscope. The light-gathering power of the telescope depends upon the area of the objective, so you can see why astronomers have made bigger and bigger telescopes. With a 40-inch telescope (one with an objective that is 40 inches in diameter) an astronomer can see twice as far as with a 20-inch telescope and can scan eight times the volume of space.

The largest refracting telescope is the 40-inch Yerkes telescope in Wisconsin which was made in 1897. Larger ob-

The 200-inch Palomar reflecting telescope is the largest of its type in the world.

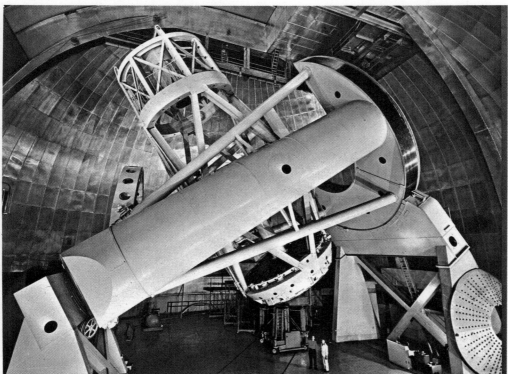

The Jodrell Bank radio telescope in Manchester, England, has a 250-foot reflector bowl and collects radio echoes from distances of 1000 million light years.

jectives are impractical due to the weight of the glass. Telescopes that see farther than the Yerkes telescope have been built by substituting a curved mirror for the convex lens objective. The largest of these *reflecting telescopes* are the 100-inch telescope on Mount Wilson (1917) and the 200-inch on Mount Palomar (1948), both in California.

The newest kind of astronomical telescope, the *radio telescope,* receives radio waves from stars, planets and nebulae which the astronomer can translate into a picture. With it he can "see" stars which are invisible to optical telescopes. Since radio waves are much longer than light waves, the receivers must be very large to scan the same volume of space as the largest reflecting telescopes. The Naval Research Laboratory radio telescope under construction at Sugar Grove, West Virginia will be the largest in the world. Its reflector will be 600 feet in diameter and over seven acres in area. It will not be able to "see" very much farther than the Palomar telescope nor as distinctly. However, it will be able to "see" things that Palomar cannot.

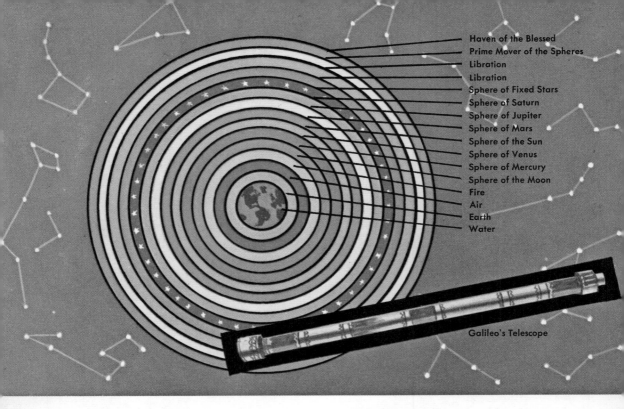

Haven of the Blessed
Prime Mover of the Spheres
Libration
Libration
Sphere of Fixed Stars
Sphere of Saturn
Sphere of Jupiter
Sphere of Mars
Sphere of the Sun
Sphere of Venus
Sphere of Mercury
Sphere of the Moon
Fire
Air
Earth
Water

Galileo's Telescope

The Greek astronomers believed that all heavenly bodies revolved about the earth. Galileo's telescope (insert) helped to disprove this theory centuries later.

Galileo Galilei was the first person to use a telescope to see farther into the heavens. His instrument magnified about five times and was similar to present day opera glasses or field glasses. With this home made telescope he saw things that startled the Europeans of 1610. He discovered that the moon was not perfectly smooth but had mountains and craters. He discovered four moons circling the planet Jupiter. (Eight more have been discovered since.) He realized that Venus must shine by light reflected from the sun instead of making its own light as the Greeks had taught.

Man, looking at the sky with the unaided eye, can see over 6000 identifiable points of light on a clear night, including light that left a *nebula* nearly two million years ago. With modern telescopes he can see billions of points of light, including light which left distant galaxies several billion years ago.

Telescopes used for sighting land objects are smaller than astronomical telescopes and include a third lens between the objective and the eyepiece which causes the image to appear right side up.

Our visual world has been greatly extended by cameras and the photographs they bring us. Whether or not you have ever visited Washington and Paris you probably would recognize the White House and the Eiffel Tower. Similarly you can recognize famous people whom you have probably never met.

Cameras can take photographs of things we could never see otherwise. Photographs taken with ultraviolet light can reveal secret writing. Infrared film used in aerial cameras can penetrate haze. Camouflage which fools the eye can be uncovered by an infrared photograph. Photographs taken by x-rays show weaknesses in metals or fractures in human bones. Color films have recorded colors deep in the oceans and high in the heavens where man had never seen color before.

Have you ever seen a strip of developed motion picture film? It consists of a series of "still" pictures, called frames,

This eclipse of the moon is an excellent example of time-lapse photography.

each slightly different from the one before. When these still pictures are projected onto the screen one after the other at the rate of 24 frames per second, we get the illusion of movement with which we are all familiar. This illusion is possible because of the persistence of vision in the cells of the retina.

Motion pictures, like still pictures, show us things we could never see otherwise. A motion picture taken at 48 frames per second and projected on the screen at 24 frames per second gives the effect of "slow motion." This enables us to see exactly how very fast motions take place. Professional tennis players, baseball players, and divers study slow-motion films to improve their form.

Special motion picture cameras have been invented which take one frame every few minutes or every few hours of a stationary subject. By means of *time-lapse photography* we can see a flower literally burst into bloom or watch a caterpillar hatch into a butterfly.

Cameras can go where people cannot. A camera can be lowered down a narrow drill shaft to photograph the inside wall of the shaft. Camera-carrying rockets are photographing outer space from positions man has not yet achieved.

No one knows all the facts about the complicated process of how we see. Many scientists and technicians from all over the world have contributed to our knowledge of vision and are continuing their work to help us learn about the complex processes of vision.

INDEX

PICTURE CREDITS. *New York Public Library,* title page; Josef Muench, p. 6; *Shostal* (Ray Manley), p. 13; *Institute for International Research,* Princeton, N. J., p. 18; *John Wiley & Sons,* N. Y., pp. 7, 21 (Fig. 16, 17), 32; *National Museum of Modern Art, Paris* (Robert Doisneau-Rapho Guillumette), p. 22; *American Optical Company,* pp. 29-30, 37, 39, 40, 41t.l., 42, 44, 46; *The Bettmann Archive,* p. 38, 41b.; *Charles Pfizer & Co.,* N. Y., p. 48t.l., b.r.; *Parke, Davis & Co.,* Detroit, p. 48t.r.; *Siemens & Halske AG,* West Germany, p. 49; *Wilson & MacPherson Hole,* p. 50; *British Information Services,* p. 51; *Minneapolis Star* (Roy E. Swan), p. 53.